Italic
HANDWRITING SERIES
Third Edition
BOOK A

by

Barbara Getty and Inga Dubay

Continuing Education Press
Portland State University
Portland, Oregon

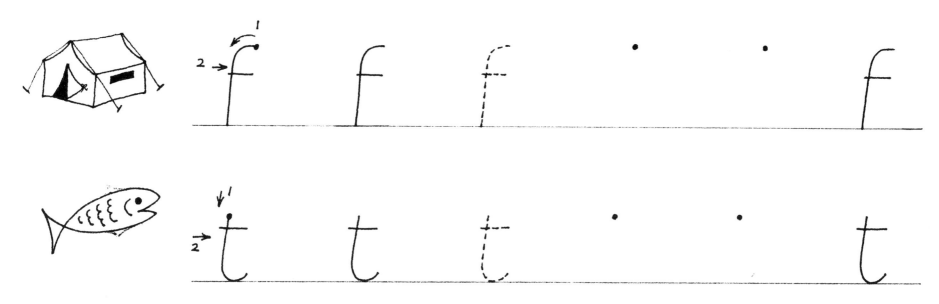

f f f · · f

t t t · · t

b c l

m k y

s n e

v d w

*TOP TWO LINES: Ask the student to draw a line from the picture
to the letter that stands for the correct beginning sound.*

*BOTTOM LINE: Ask the student to circle the letter that
stands for the beginning sound of the picture.*

CONTENTS

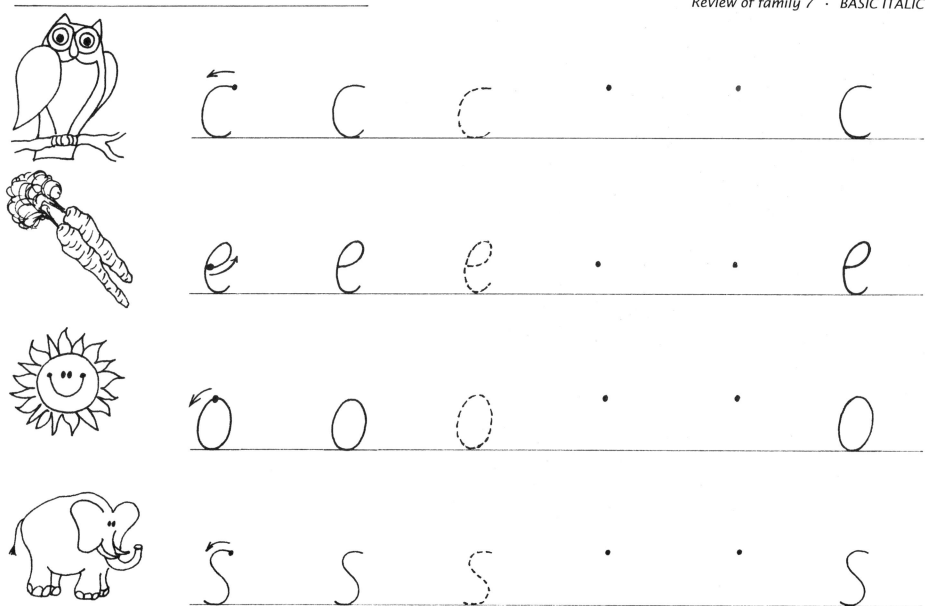

Ask the student to draw a line from the picture to the letter that stands for the correct beginning sound.

INTRODUCTION

This is the first of seven books providing instruction in basic italic handwriting. It is designed for the beginning student of handwriting and is recommended for preschool, kindergarten and/or early first grade.

The twenty-six lowercase letters and the twenty-six capitals are introduced one letter per page. Letters are arranged in the order of lowercase families, which group letters with similar strokes together and progress from simple to more complex forms. The matching capital letter occurs on the reverse of each lowercase page allowing introduction of both lowercase and capital together if preferred.

Each page is designed for the student to trace the models provided, write letters at the given dots, and to write a "best" letter in the empty box on each alphabet page. In the space provided at the lower left of each page, the student may write more letters, words and/or draw pictures related to the given letter. For example, the student or instructor may write a large letter with a crayon, then the student traces it several times with other colors or with his or her forefinger. The standard writing tool is the pencil although other tools such as the fiber tip pen may be used.

It is essential that the instructor provide an understanding of the dot and the arrow to assist the writer in completing the pages successfully. The self-assessment method used in the *Italic Handwriting Series* enables the student to monitor progress. Step 1, LOOK, of the three-step LOOK, PLAN, PRACTICE format can be incorporated verbally by the instructor. The student is asked to "LOOK" at the writing and affirm what is the best. See INSTRUCTION MANUAL, pp. 13, 18 & 19.

The *Italic Handwriting Series* INSTRUCTION MANUAL is to be used in conjunction with this workbook. Explanations and in-depth descriptions of lowercase letters, capitals, joins, and numerals are presented in the manual, emphasizing the shape, strokes, size, slope and spacing of the letters. Also included in the manual are: a rationale for italic handwriting, techniques for teaching and assessing handwriting, sequence of skills, handwriting activities, and a brief history of our alphabet.

BOOK B, basic italic, follows this workbook and is designed for the beginning reader. In the third book, BOOK C, basic italic letterforms are reinforced and cursive italic is introduced. BOOKS D, E, F, and G provide a complete italic basic and cursive italic handwriting program. BOOKS B, C, and/or D may also be suitable for the person learning English as a second language.

The format of this book was chosen to accommodate both the left- and right-handed writer. When open, the book fits easily on a small desk, and the writer is not encumbered with an additional page to the left or right. From day one, use desk strips and wall charts. Blackline masters are designed for supplementary practice and are available for each workbook in the series.

You can guide children toward the challenge and delight in the writing process by reading to them, modeling handwriting, providing writing materials, and especially by building enthusiasm for the letters of our alphabet and for the written word.

·abcdefghijklmnopqrstuvwxyz·

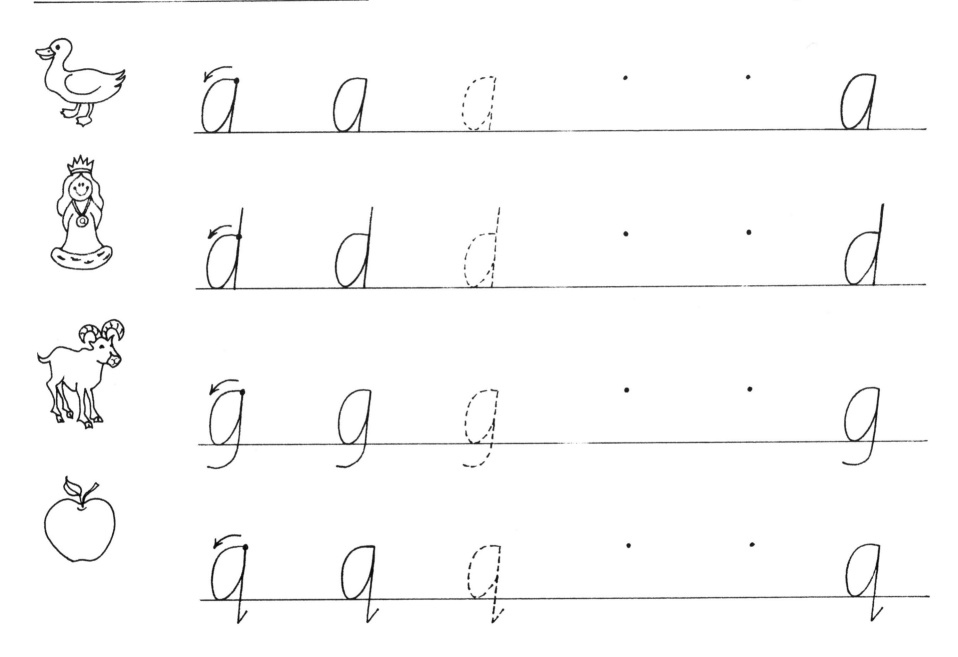

*Ask the student to draw a line from the picture to the letter
that stands for the correct beginning sound.*

REMINDERS

PENCIL HOLD

Hold the pencil with the thumb and index finger, resting it on the middle finger. Rest the shaft of the pencil near the large knuckle. Hold the tool firmly and avoid pinching. To relax the hand, tap index finger on the pencil three times. Avoid "thumb wrap" and a "death grip".

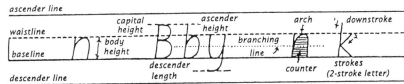

PAPER POSITION

LEFT-HANDED: If the left-handed student writes with the wrist below the writing line, turn paper clockwise so it is slanted to the right, as illustrated.

If the left-handed student writes with a hook, with the wrist above the writing line, turn the paper counter-clockwise so it is slanted to the left, as illustrated.

RIGHT-HANDED: If the student is right-handed, turn paper counter-clockwise so it is slanted to the left, as illustrated. This is similar to the right-handed position.

POSTURE

Rest feet flat on the floor and keep back comfortably straight without slumping. Rest forearms on writing surface. The student holds workbook or paper with the nonwriting hand so that the writing area is centered in the front of the student.

PRACTICE PAPER

Book A—when beginning instruction, use unlined paper to introduce letters. Then use unlined or lined paper together with workbooks.

MATERIALS

The *Italic Handwriting Series* workbooks, BOOKS A-G, and the INSTRUCTION MANUAL constitute a step-by-step program. Related materials consist of:

1. BLACKLINE MASTERS/WORKSHEETS - half sheets for introduction to, or review of, workbook pages.
2. CLASSROOM WALL CHARTS - basic & cursive italic.
3. DESK STRIPS - basic & cursive italic.
4. MOVEABLE ALPHABET

VOCABULARY

DIRECT INSTRUCTION

Several sessions of direct instruction each week are essential for a successful program. BOOK A – 5 to 10 minute sessions a day are recommended, see INSTRUCTION MANUAL, pp. 18-19

- SHAPE & STROKE SEQUENCE – teach basic italic in letter family groups, or according to the reading program in grade 1.
- SLOPE – encourage a consistent letter slope. Vertical letters (0° slope) may be the easiest to teach to beginning writers.
- SIZE – At first, allow students to write letters any size they wish on unlined paper, then introduce the workbook. A recommended progression through this book is one letter (lowercase and/or capital) per week.

SPACING

BOOKS A–If students are writing words: leave a space about the width of a student's two fingers between words.

ASSESSMENT

The *Italic Handwriting Series* provides a self-assessment process, LOOK, PLAN, PRACTICE, to enable the student to monitor progress. LOOK, step 1, of this process begins on the student page in BOOK B. However, since BOOK A is for the beginning writer, no assessment references are made on student pages. Therefore, verbally direct your students to LOOK at their own writing and circle a "best" letter on a particular line or page.

The teacher may encourage students to award themselves a smiling face at the top of the page when they notice self-improvement.

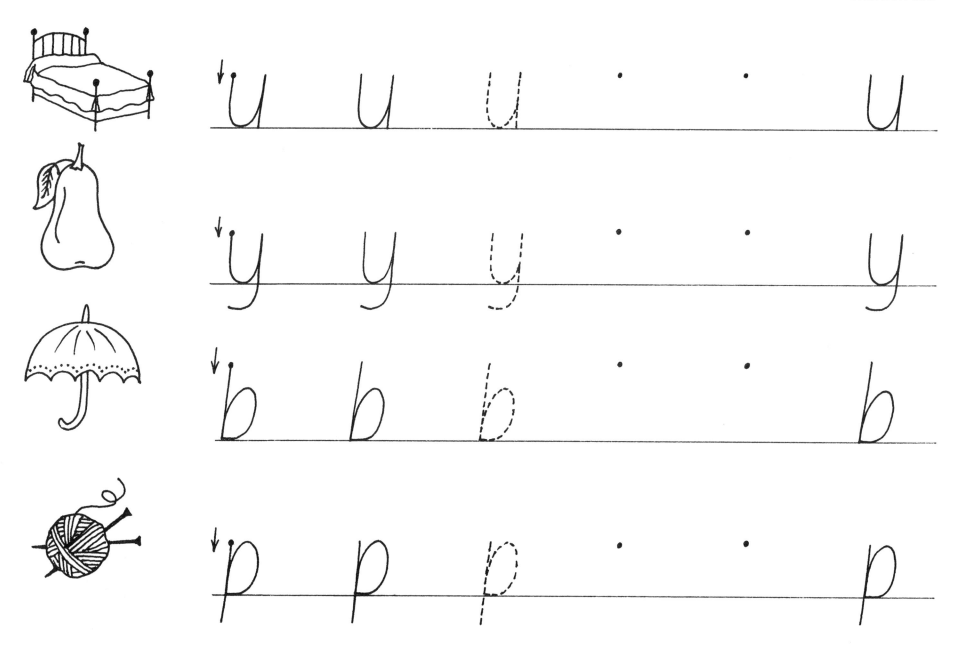

BASIC ITALIC ALPHABET

All letters written in one stroke unless otherwise indicated.

Aa Bb Cc Dd Ee Ff Gg

or (a)   *alternate 2-stroke e*

Hh Ii Jj Kk Ll Mm

or   or

Nn Oo Pp Qq Rr Ss Tt

or   or

Uu Vv Ww Xx Yy Zz

0 1 2 3 4 5 6 7 8 9

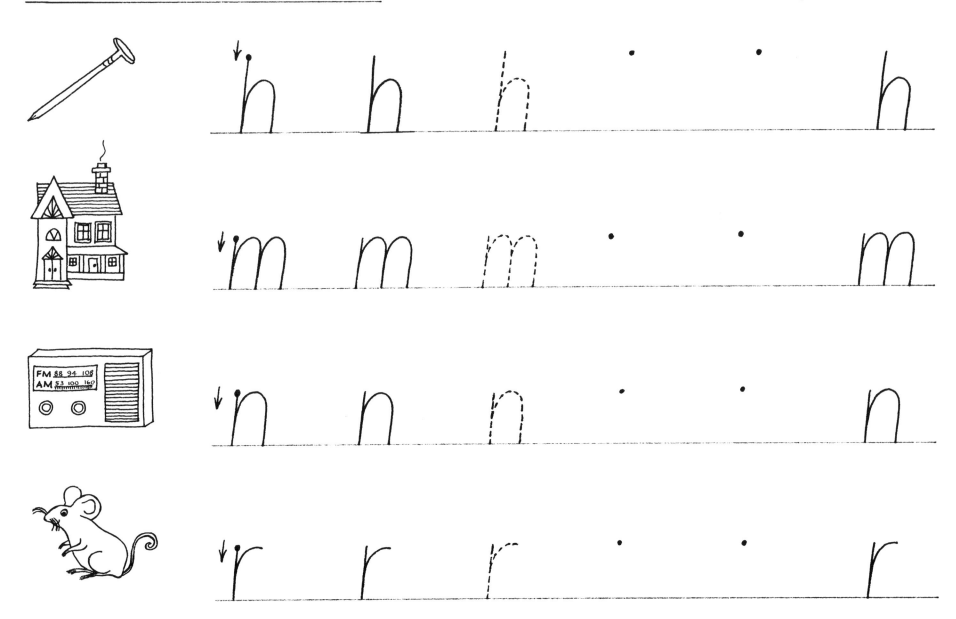

Ask the student to draw a line from the picture to the letter that stands for the correct beginning sound.

61

Learning how to write involves much more than learning to write letters. It is a sophisticated, complex process involving learning letterforms, learning how to space within and between words, and learning how to organize writing on a page. Research indicates that there exists an almost perfect correlation between measures evaluating the children's *awareness* of their fingers and the ability to *use* their fingers in precise manual skills.

Ways to determine manual ability

To assist young students increase awareness of their hands and fingers, and to help you, the teacher, evaluate students' manual skills, have your students perform these tasks:

1. Direct the students to touch each of their fingers to their thumb, in order, from the first to the little finger. (By the age of six years, most children should be able to complete this exercise using one or both hands at a time.)

2. Have the students connect two dots that are spaced approximately eight inches apart on a page. (Most children of five years can accomplish this. However, if the student draws beyond the second dot or draws an unusually shaky line when nearing the second dot, it may indicate potential deficiencies in handwriting skills.)

Ways to improve kinesthetic perception of the hands

1. Unstructured clay modeling facilitates a student's perception of his or her hands. Encourage the student to manipulate the clay in every possible way—squeezing, flattening, poking, making shapes, etc.

2. To heighten the student's perception of shape, use a box in which a variety of small objects are placed for the student to feel but not see.

   a. Ask the student to reach in the box and find an unseen object that matches the one he or she is looking at.

   b. Direct the student to locate in the box an object that you or another student has described.

   c. Ask the student to find two objects with similar characteristics— two fuzzy objects, two heavy objects, two small objects, etc.

3. Draw several circles on a sheet of paper. To determine the student's ability to aim the finger and hand and also to point, have the student place dots in the circles with a pencil, pen, or crayon. Vary the difficulty of this task by increasing or decreasing the size of the circles or increasing the rate at which the dots are made. (The student must be able to point at a given or imaginary point in order to begin the stroke of a letter.)

Ways to confirm hand-eye tracking skills

The ability to control continuous hand movements while drawing lines of varying difficulty is basic to handwriting. If you are able to detect problems as the student completes the following tasks and are able to obtain appropriate assistance for the student, subsequent difficulties may be avoided.

1. Demonstrate drawing parallel lines. Then direct the student to draw parallel lines of a given length, first at a relaxed pace then at a faster one.

2. Direct the student to draw two curved lines equal in distance from one another. Later require more difficult shapes that combine straight lines, angles, and/or curves.

3. Direct the student to connect numbered dots on a sheet of paper that require horizontal, vertical and lateral movements. Place the paper in front of the student, close to the dominant hand. Later, space the dots further apart and require the student to cross the midline of his or her body. This latter task may cause the neurologically challenged student some difficulty.

The above evaluative tasks may be of help in assisting the learning of handwriting and in discovering deficiencies.

(See INSTRUCTION MANUAL, p. 13, for more suggestions concerning the beginning writer.)

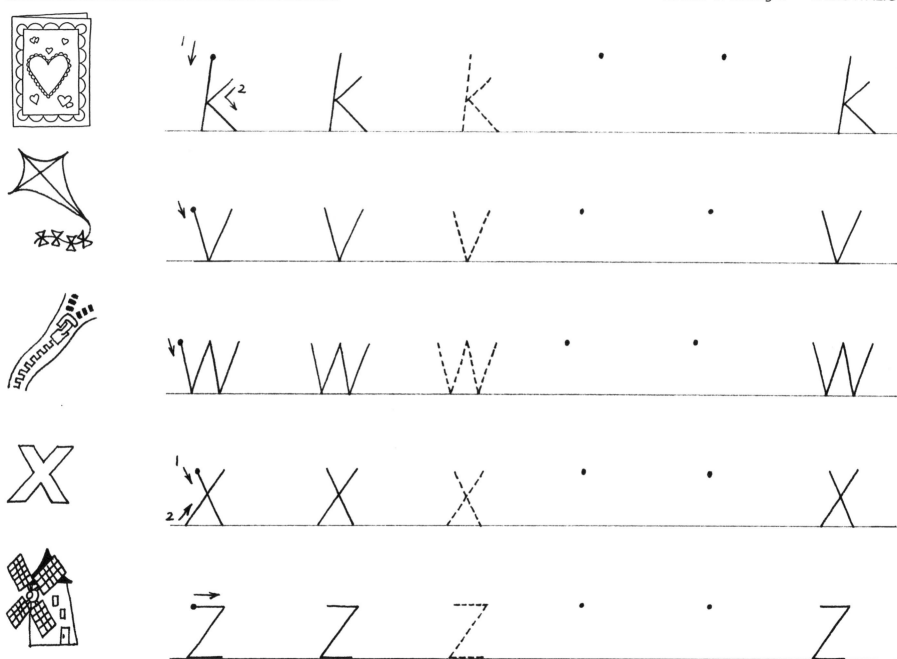

Ask the student to draw a line from the picture to the letter
that stands for the correct beginning sound.

BASIC SHAPES

Before the student begins writing in BOOK A, the authors recommend that the student practice the following shapes on unlined paper, one shape at a time. Allow the student to write each shape any size at first. Later, ask the student to write very large and very small forms of that same shape. We suggest the student also practice these shapes on a chalkboard and/or in cornmeal. (See INSTRUCTION MANUAL, "*Activity,*" pp. 35 & 41.)

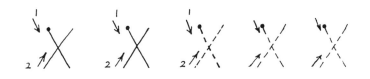

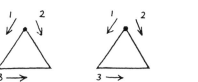

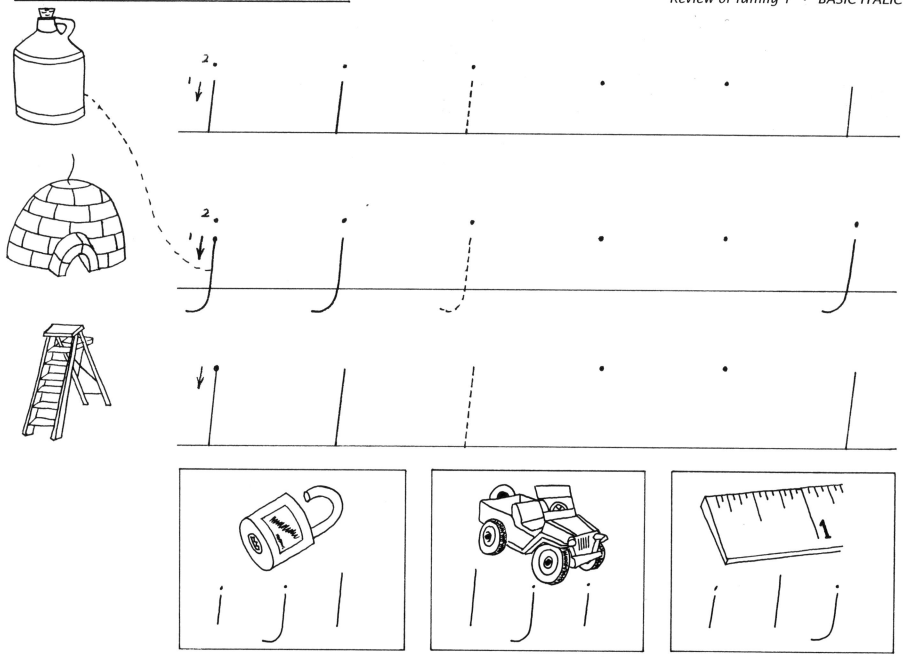

*TOP THREE LINES: Ask the student to draw a line from the picture
to the letter that stands for the correct beginning sound.*

*BOTTOM LINE: Ask the student to circle the letter that
stands for the beginning sound of the picture.*

59

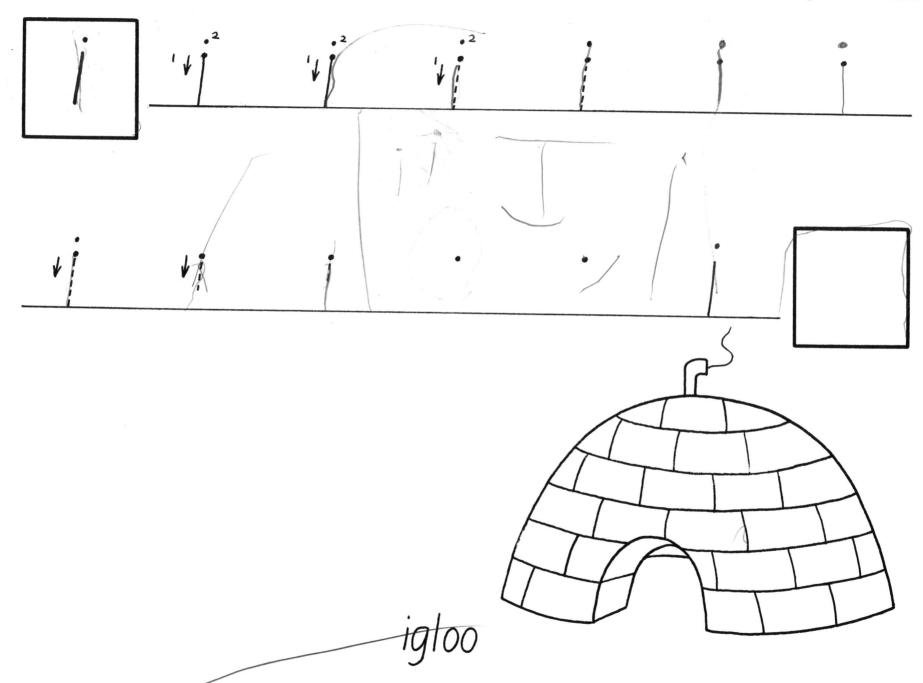

igloo

Use work space above for more letters, words and/or pictures.

Ice Cream

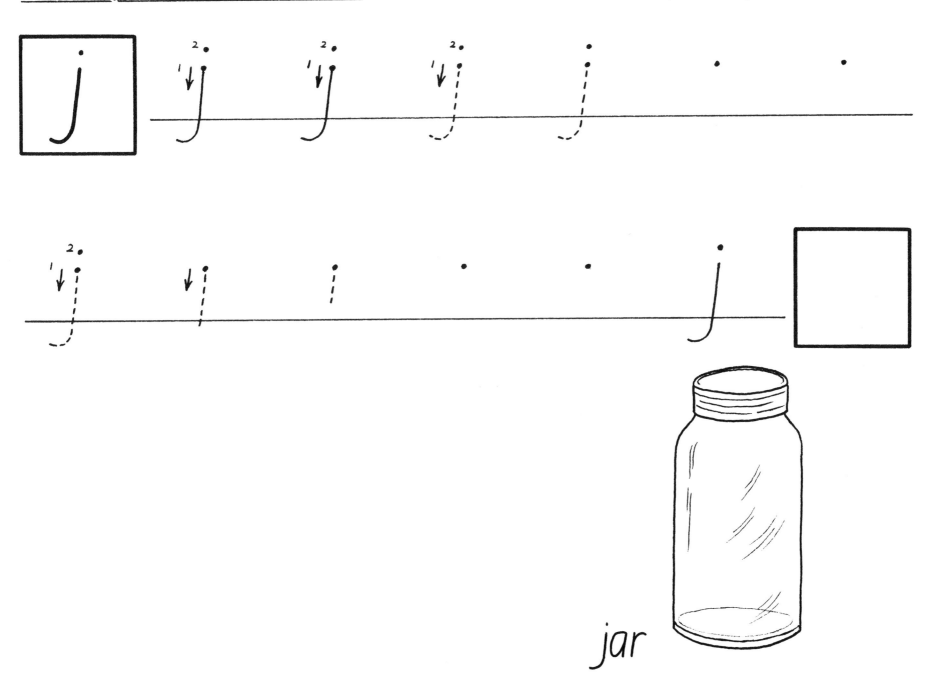

jar

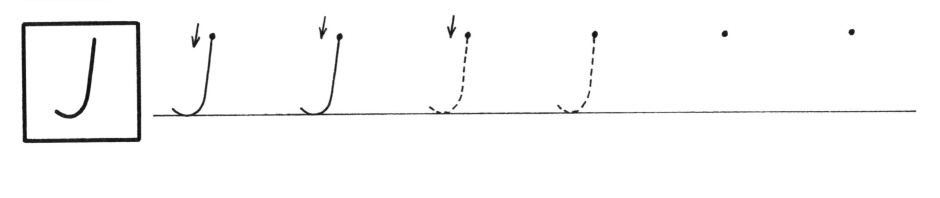

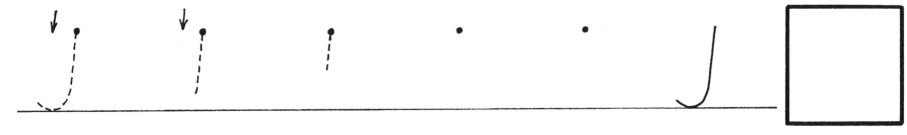

Jack-in-the-box

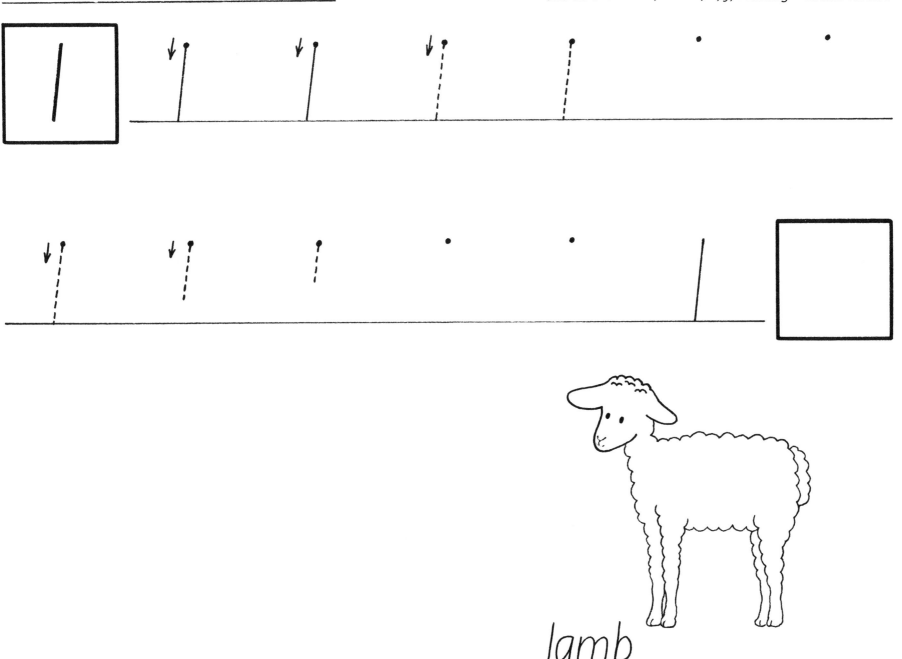

lamb

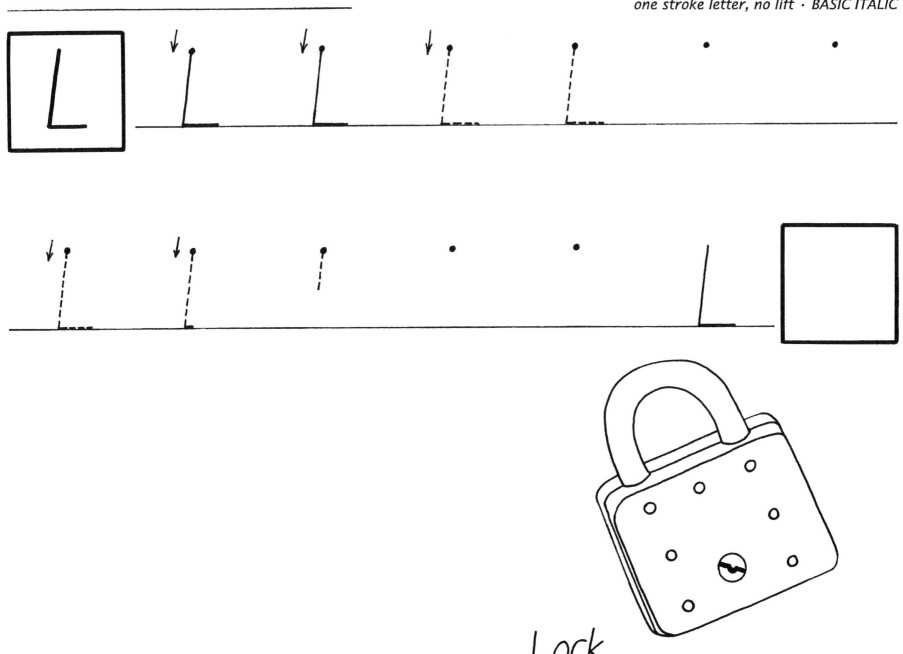

Lock

k

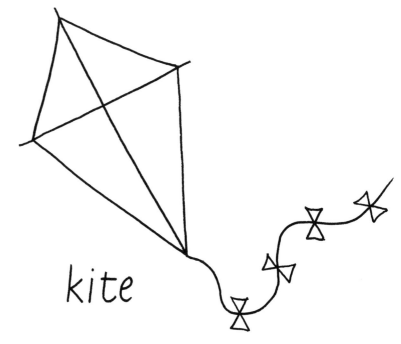

kite

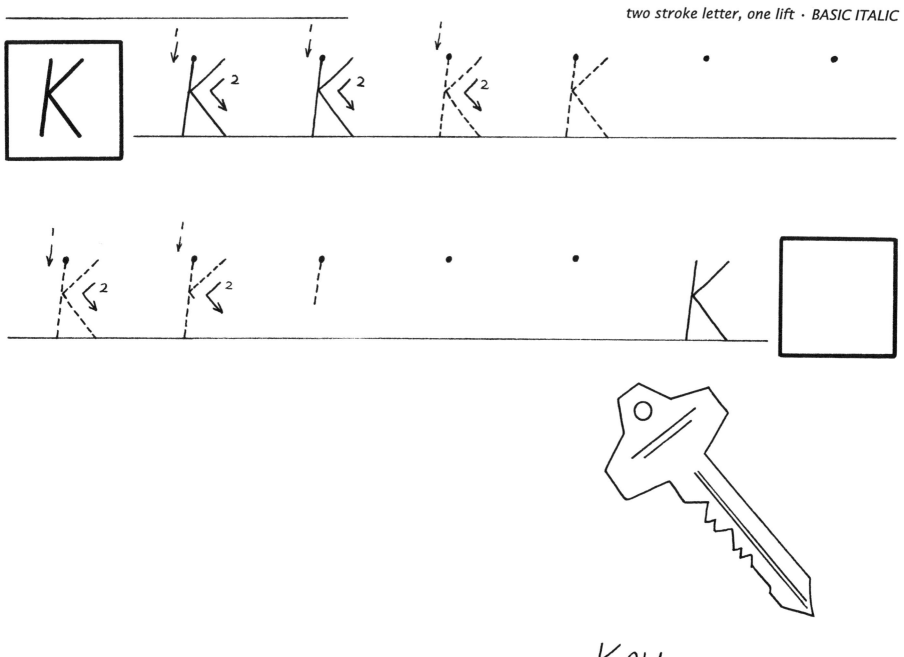

Key

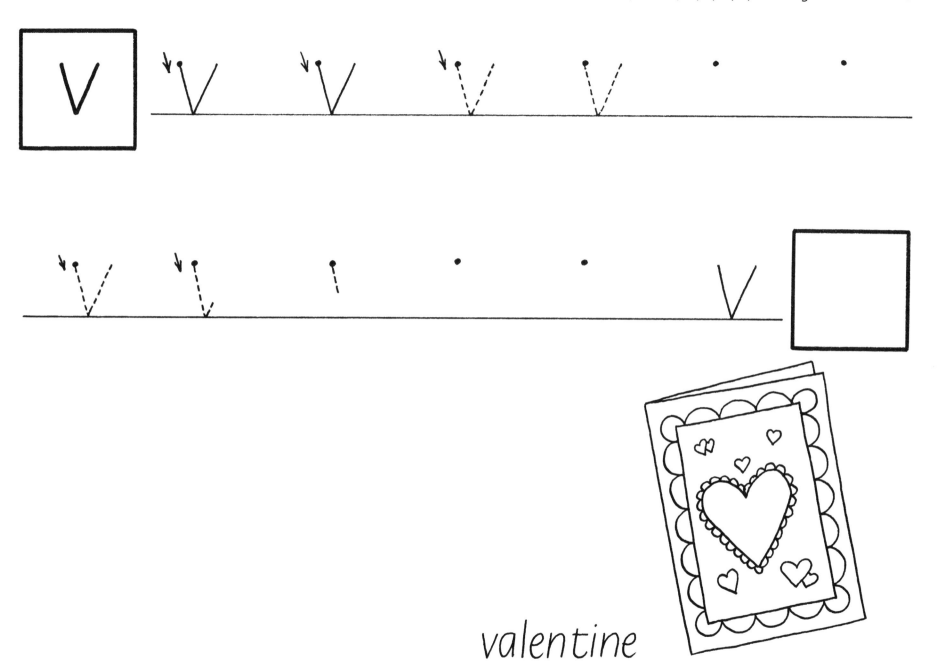

valentine

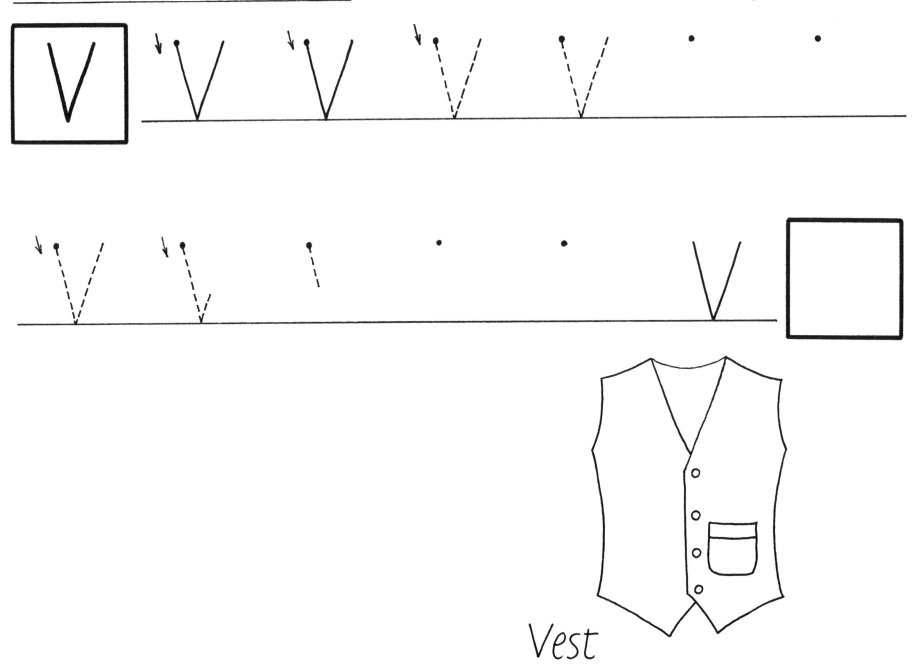

Vest

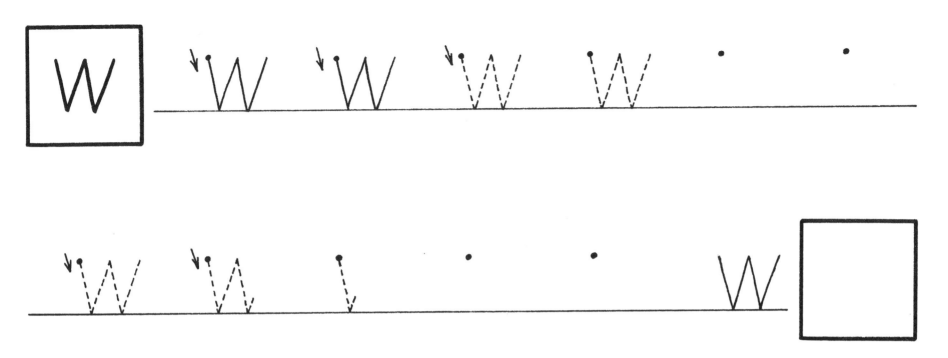

wagon

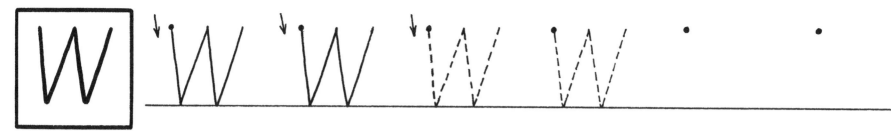

W W W W W

W W V W

Watch

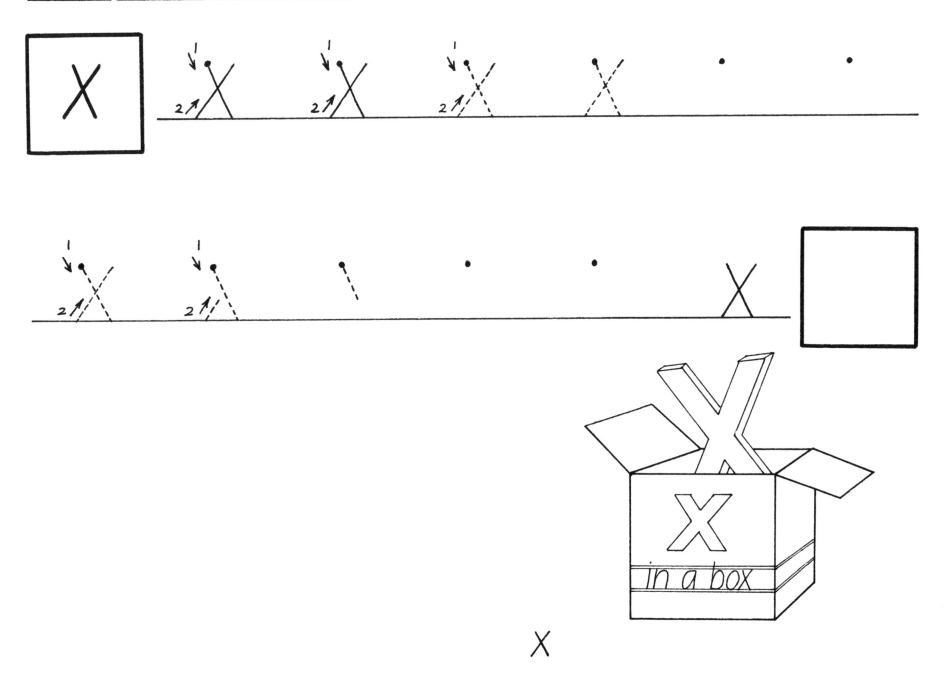

X in a box

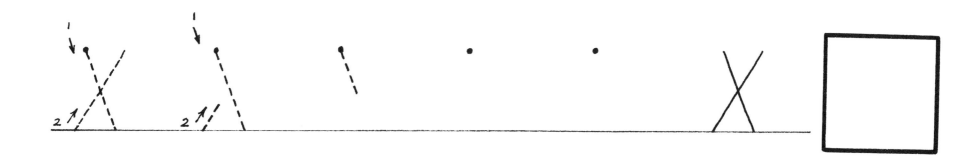

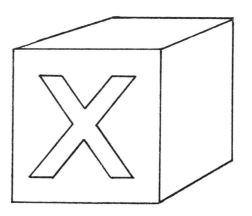

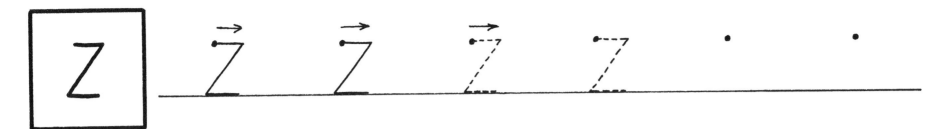

Z   z   z   z   z

z   z

zebra

Z

Z Z Z Z

Z Z Z Z

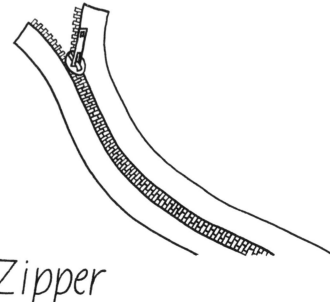

Zipper

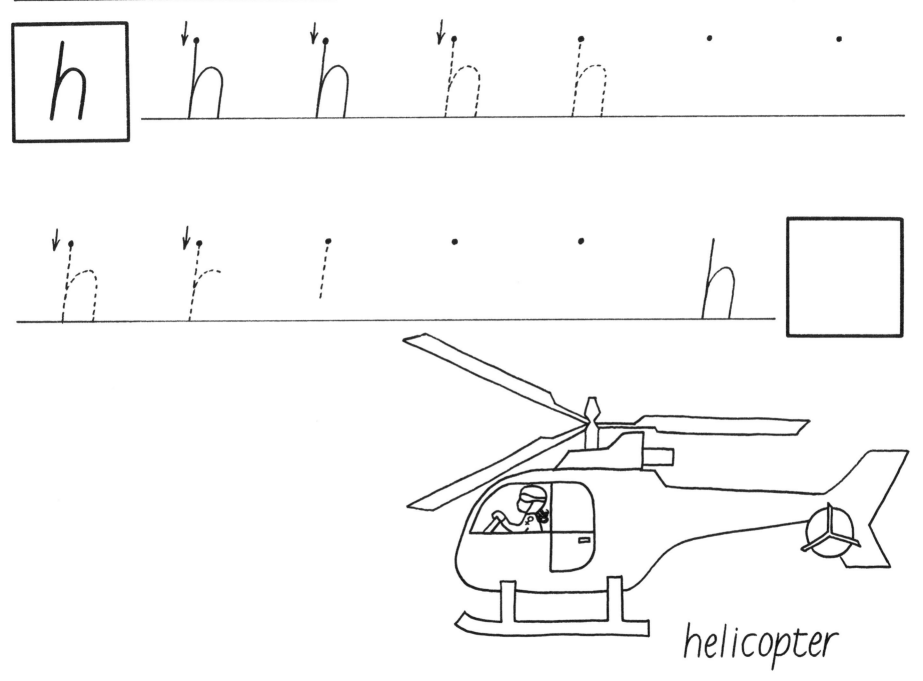

helicopter

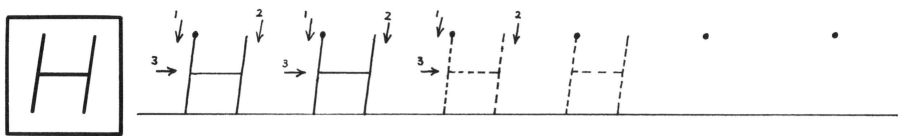

Hammer

m

↓'m ↓'m 'm m · ·

↓'m ↓'r 'r · · m

mouse

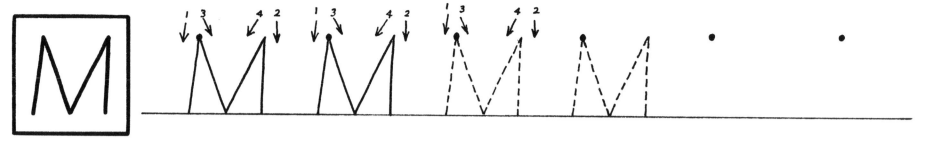

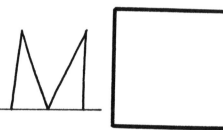

Mittens

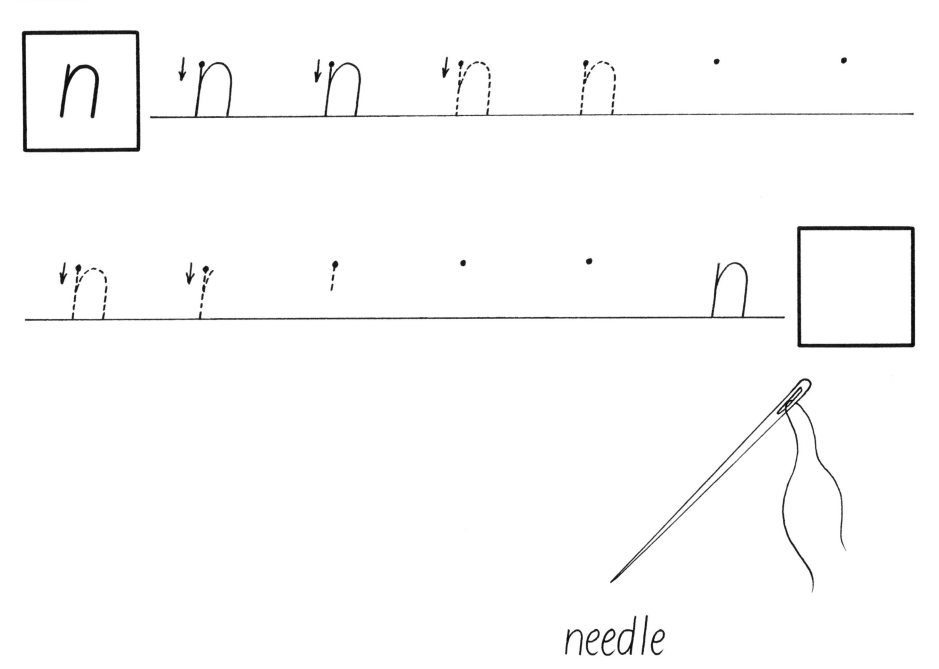

needle

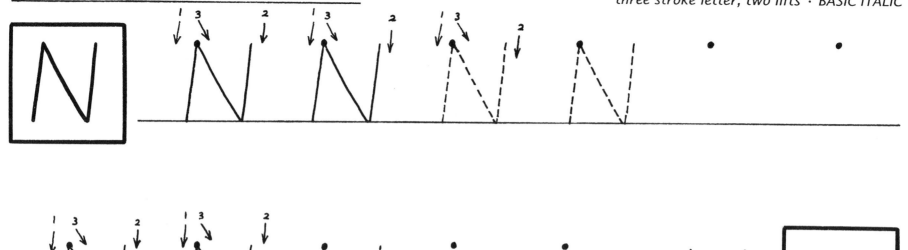

Net

r

rabbit

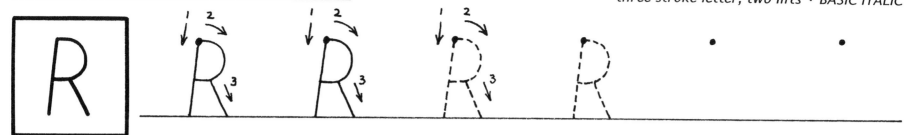

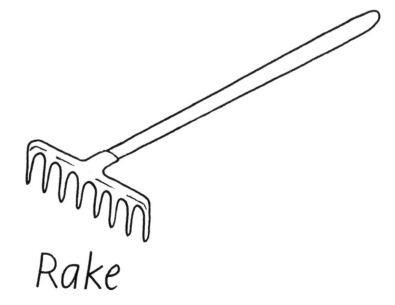

Rake

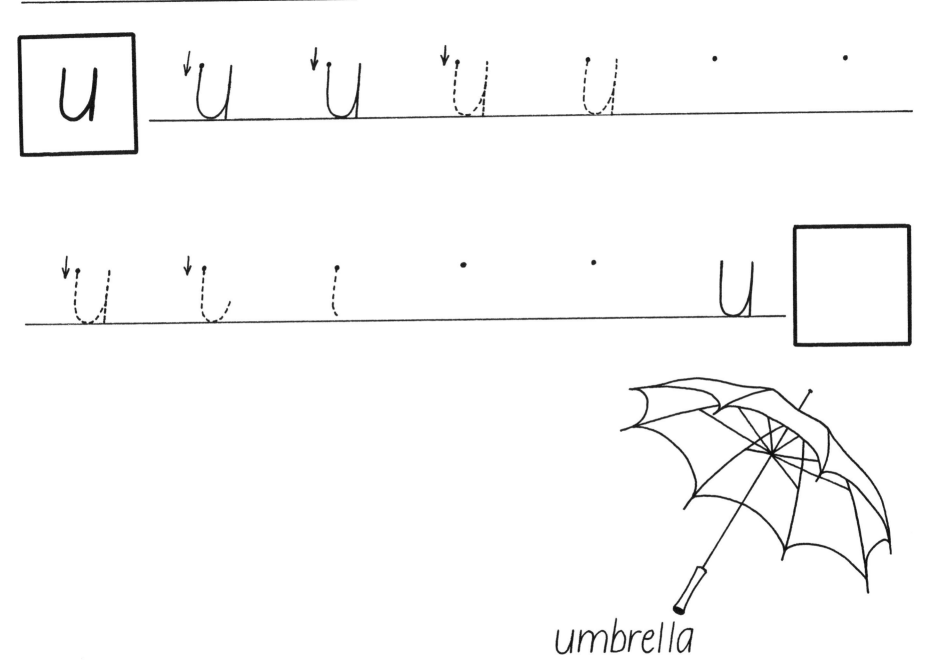

umbrella

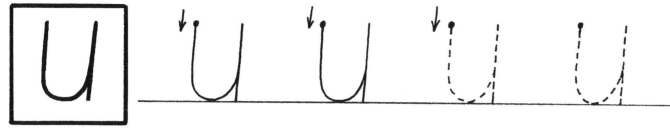

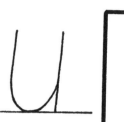

Ukulele

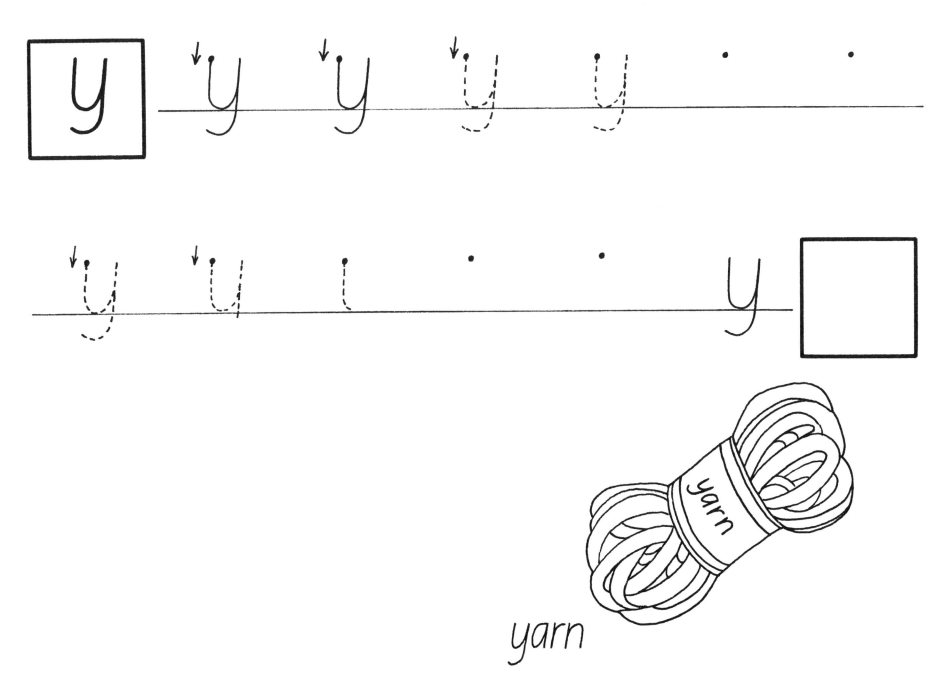

yarn

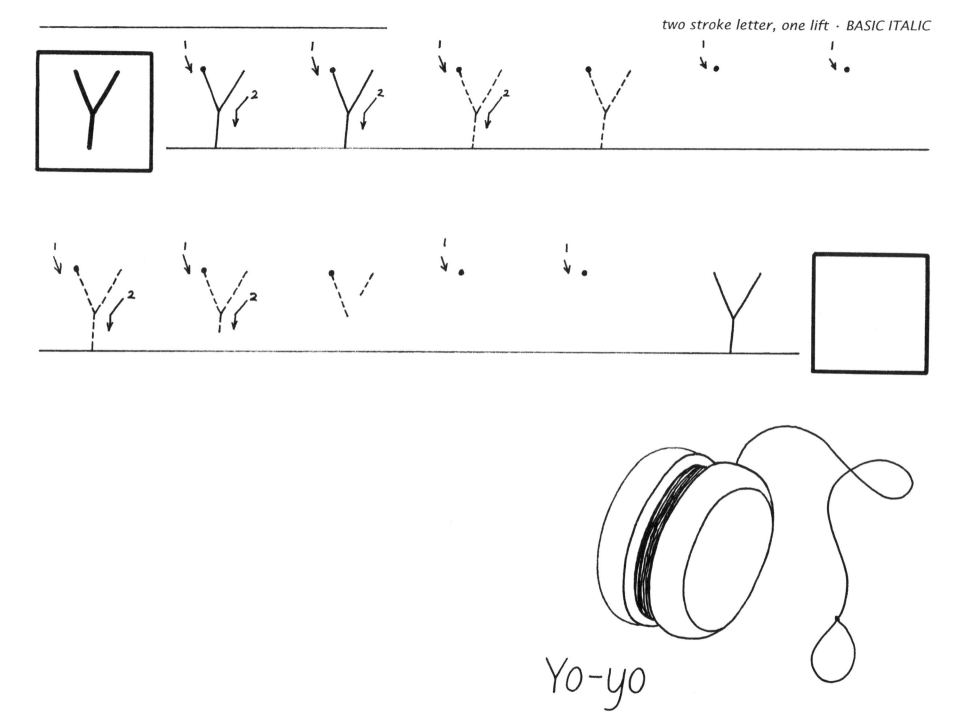

Yo-yo

apple

14mm · A

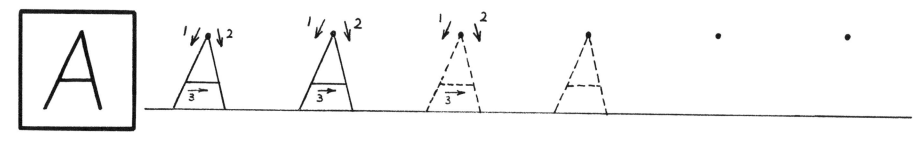

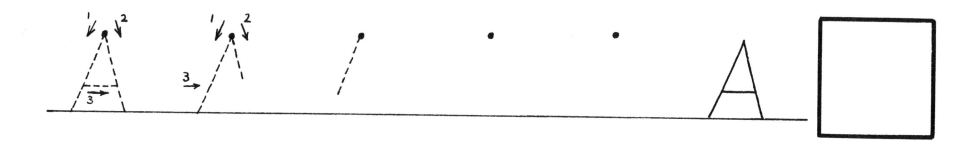

Alligator

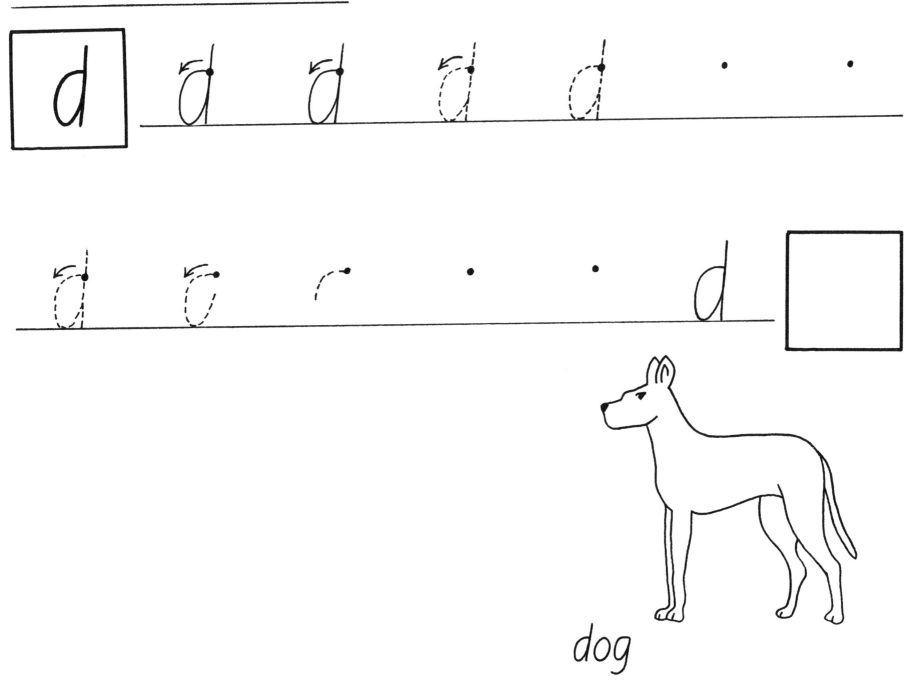

dog

Dinosaur

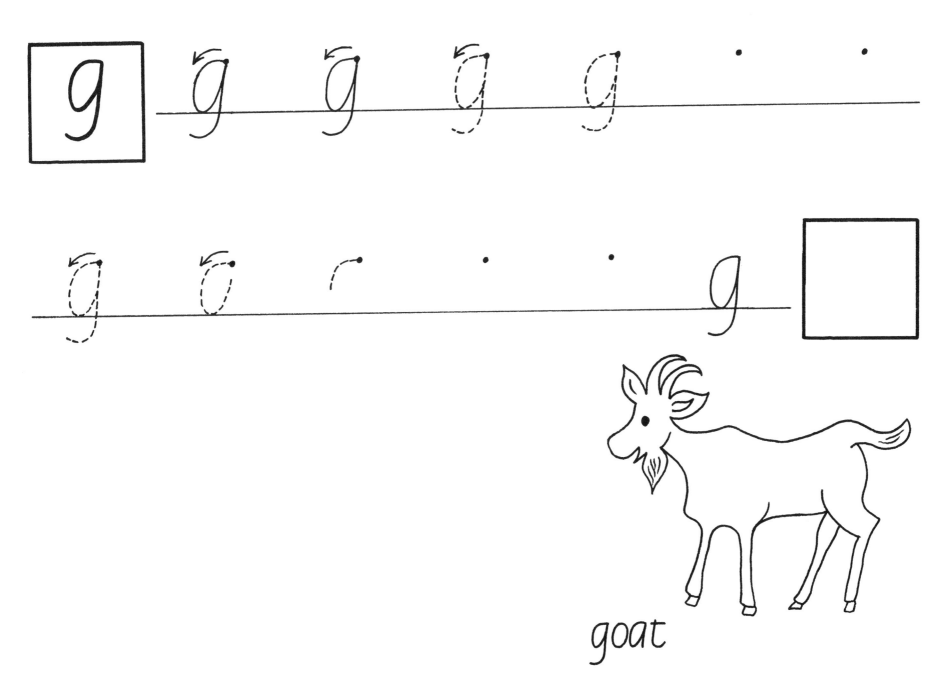

goat

14mm · A

Gate

© Getty/Dubay 1994

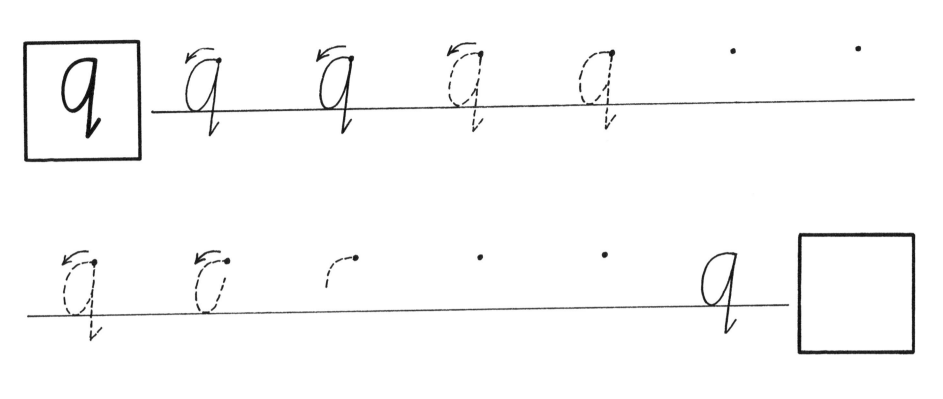

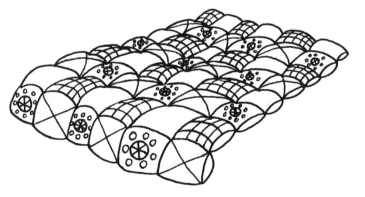

quilt

14mm · A

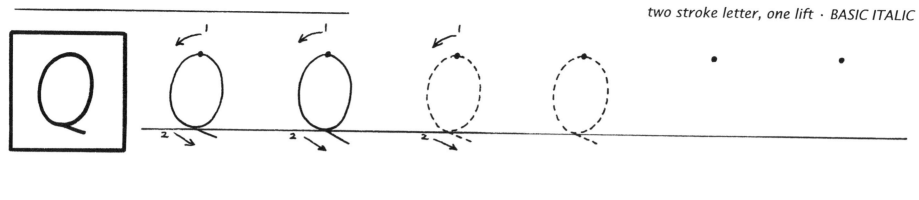

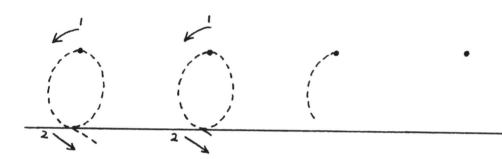

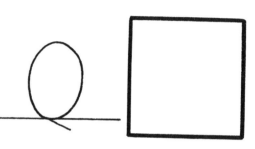

Queen

b b b b b · ·

b r i · · b

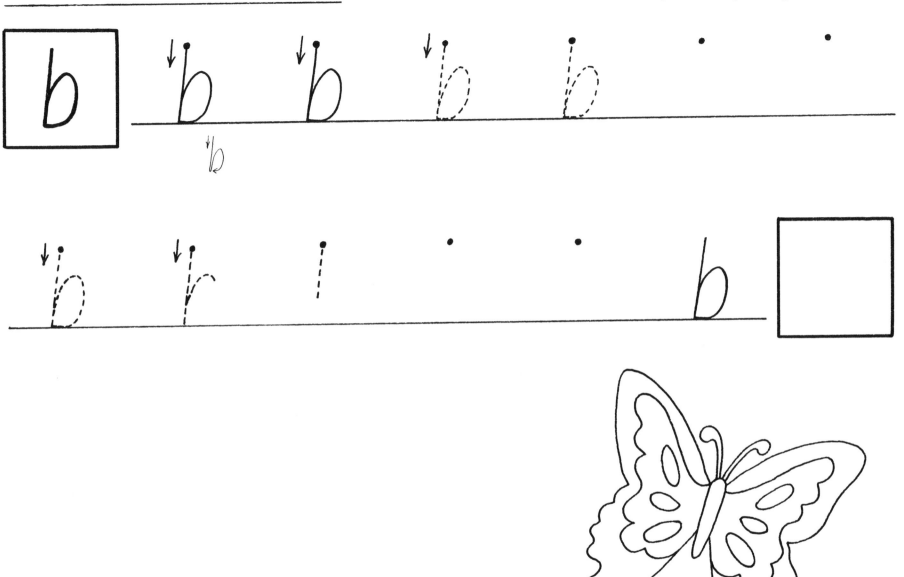

butterfly

14mm · A

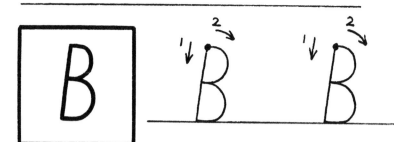

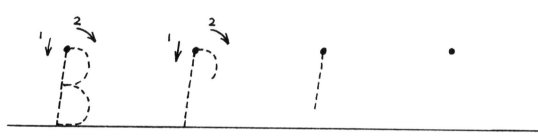

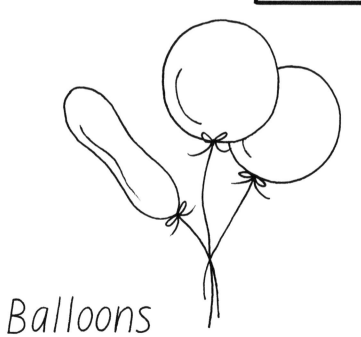

Balloons

© Getty/Dubay 1994

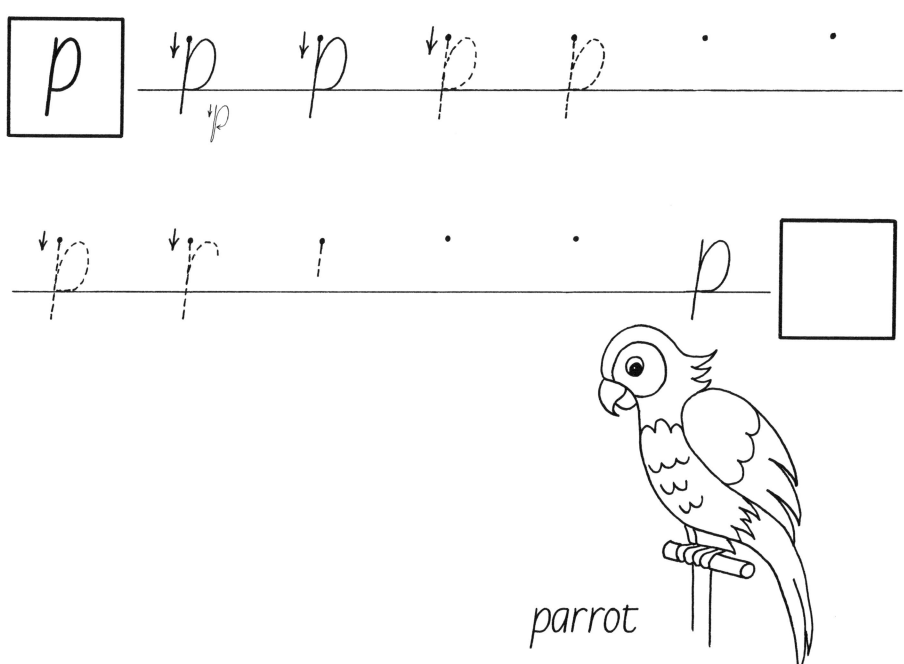

parrot

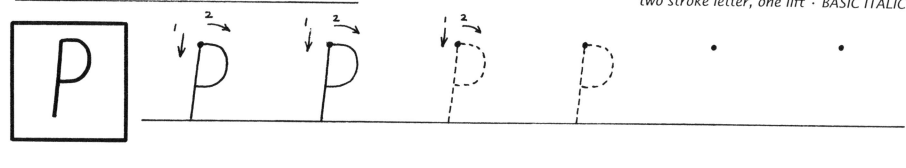

P

Peacock

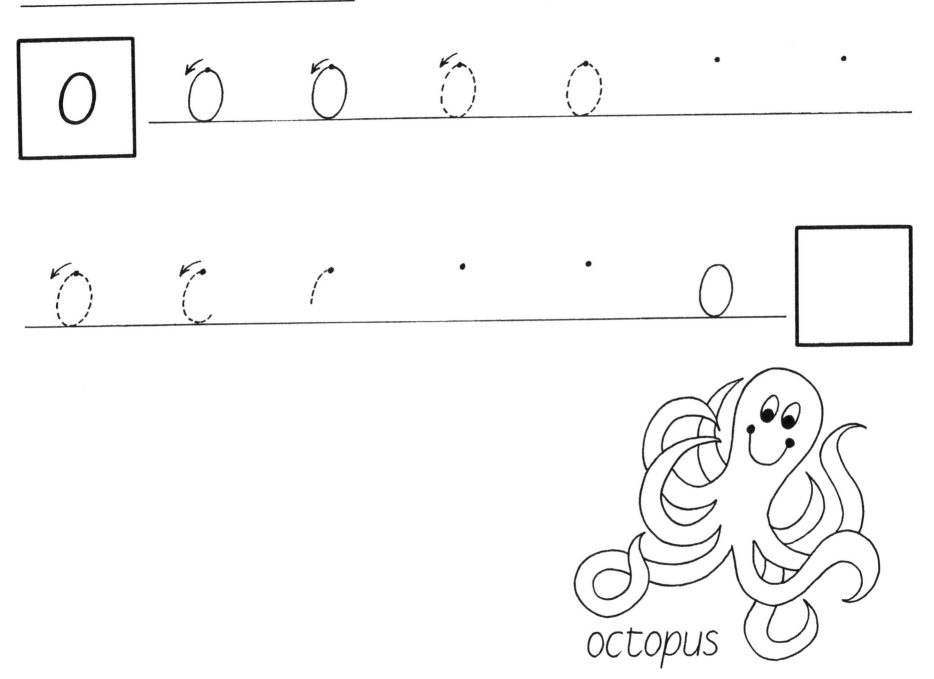

octopus

14mm · A

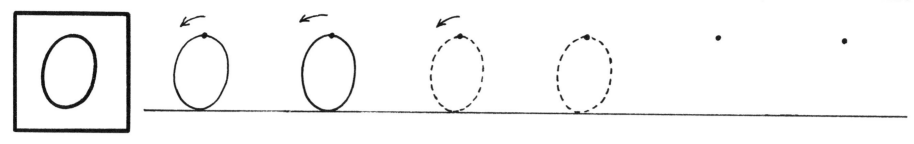

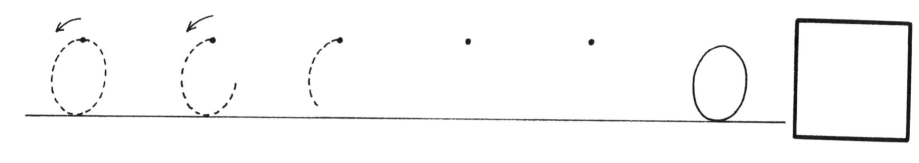

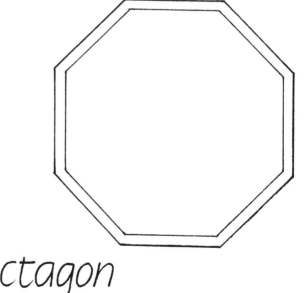

Octagon

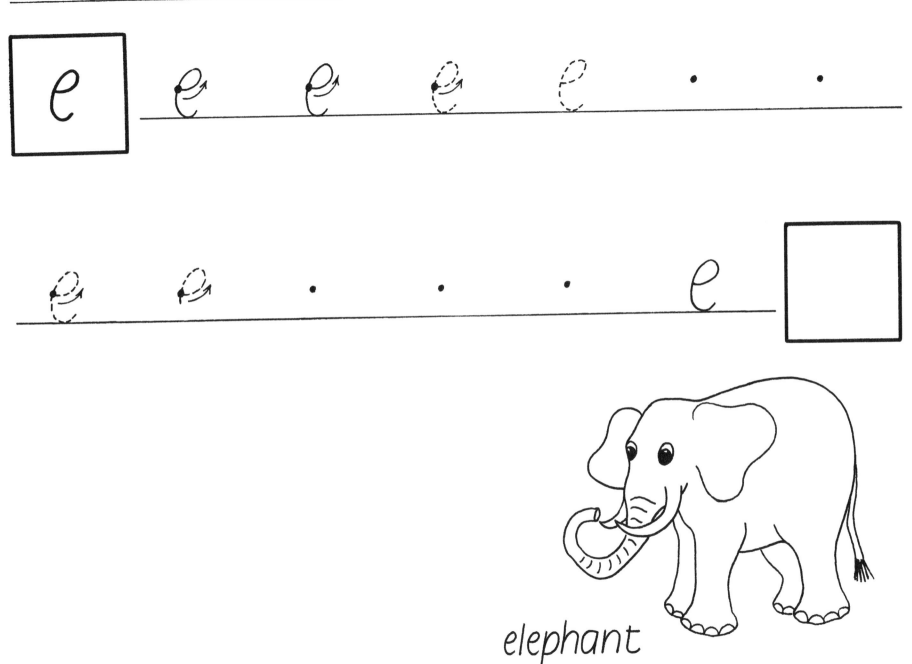

elephant

14mm · A

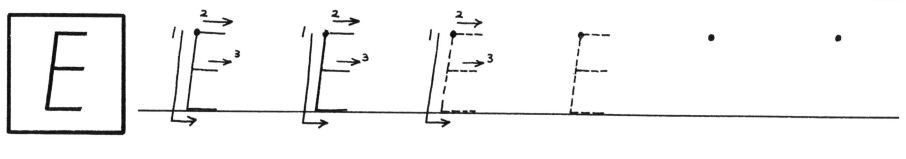

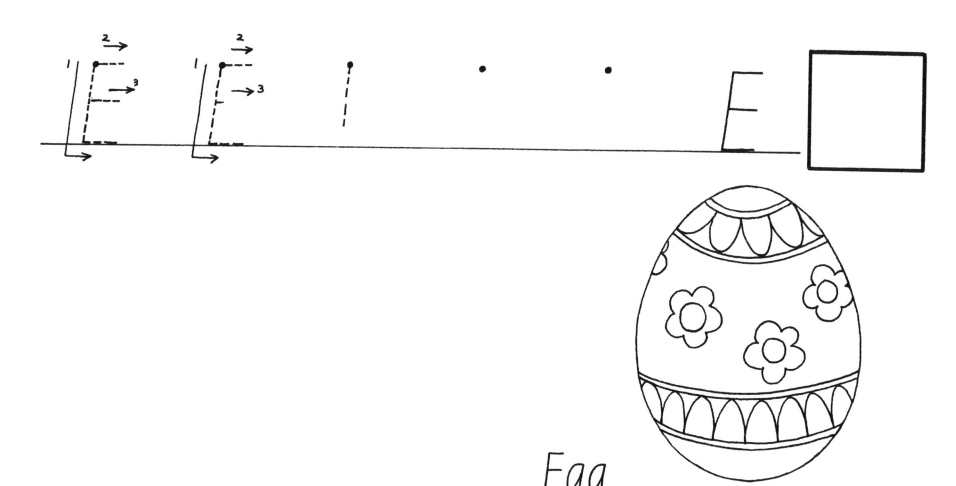

Egg

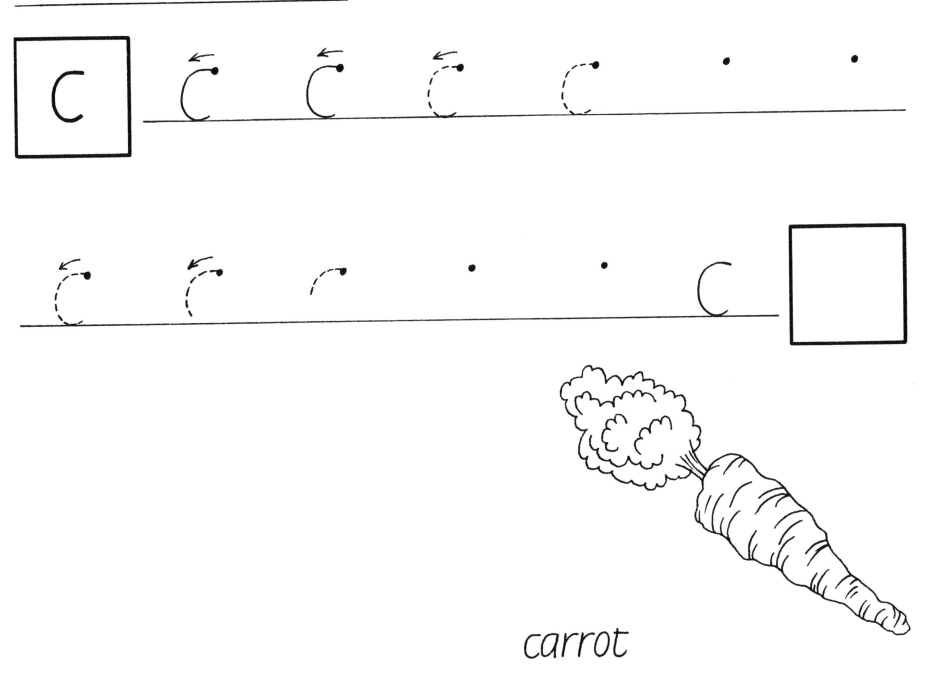

carrot

14mm · A

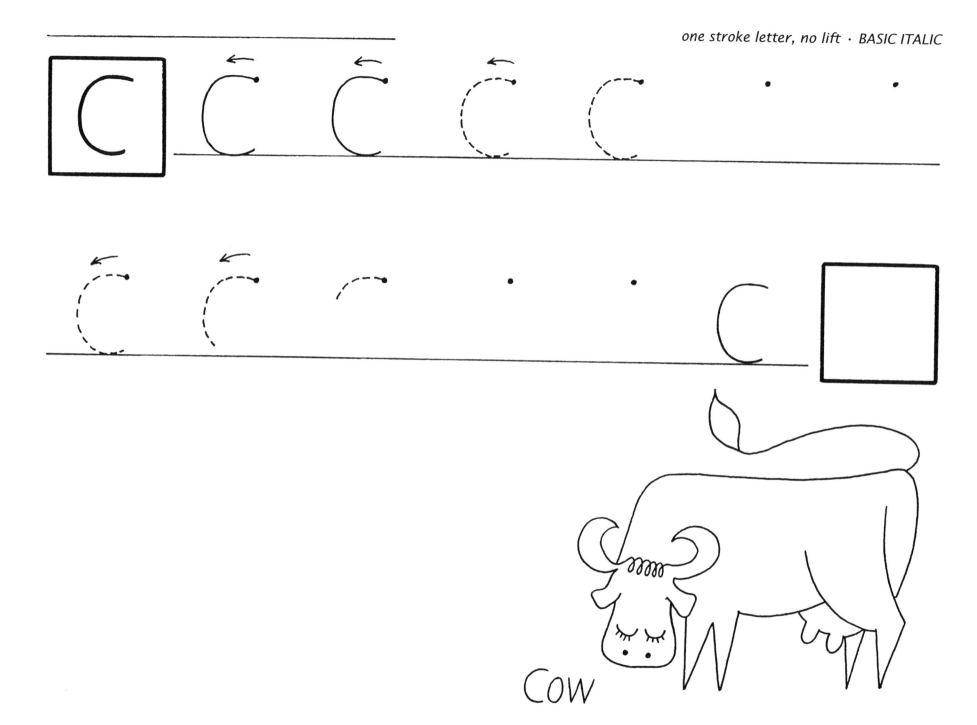

Cow

S   s   s   s   s   ·   ·

s   s   ·   ·   ·   s

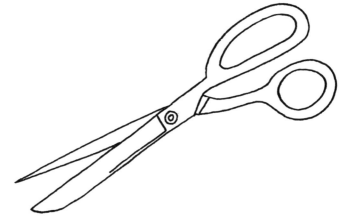

scissors

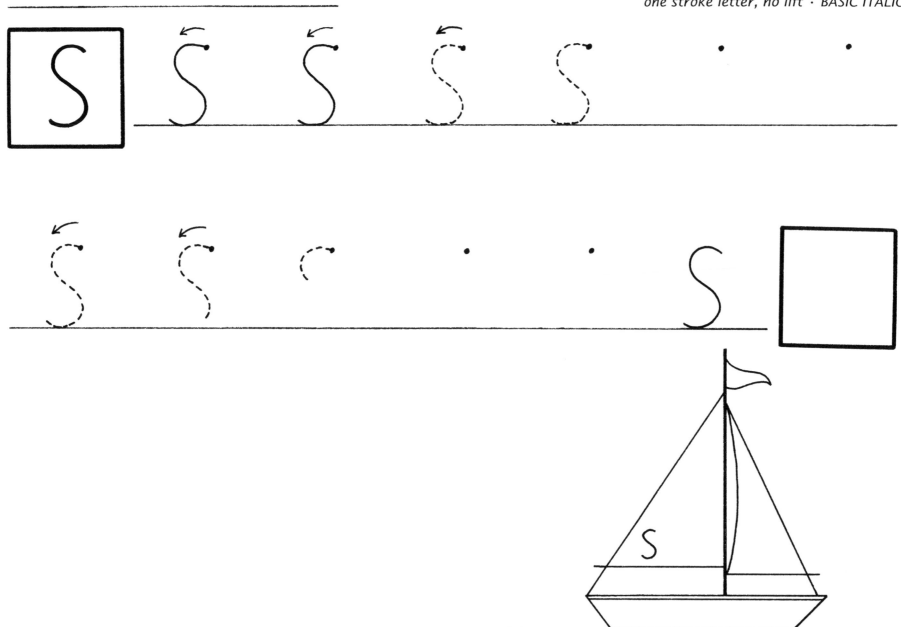

Sailboat

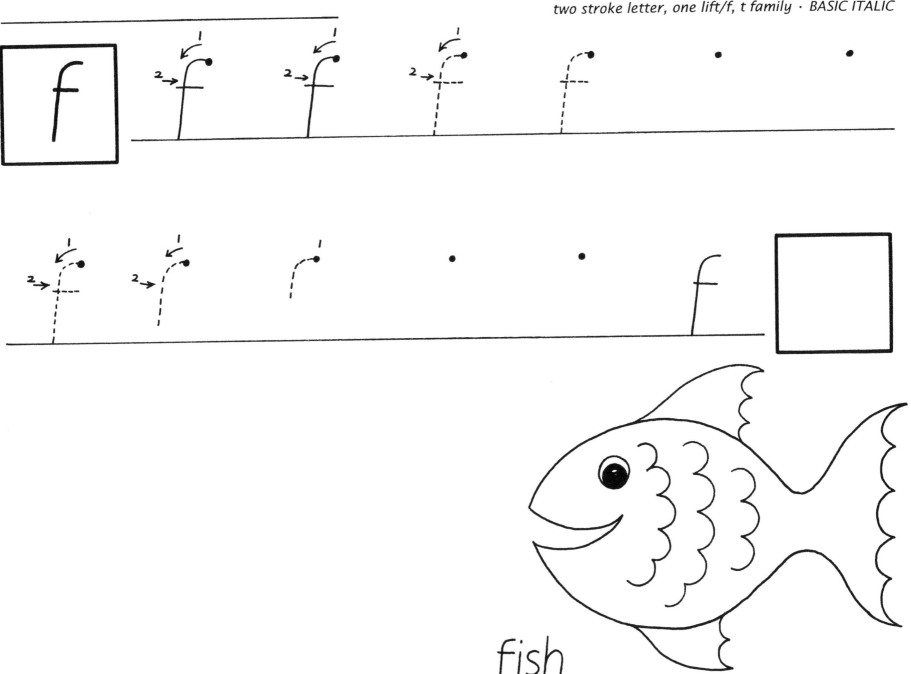

fish

14mm · A   25

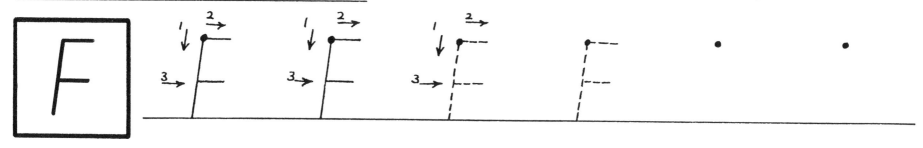

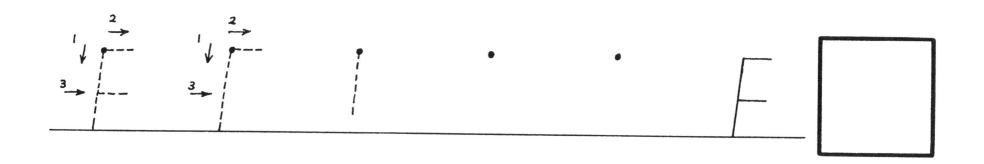

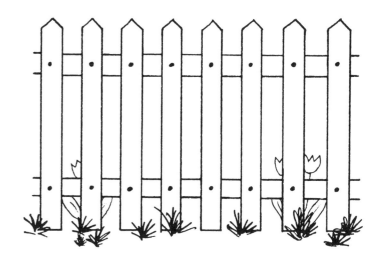

Fence

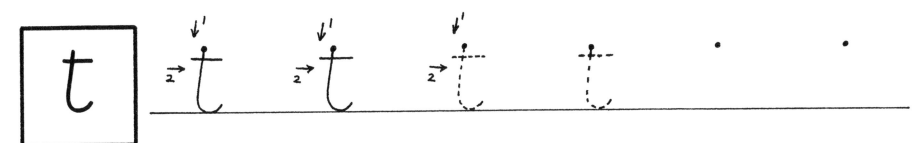

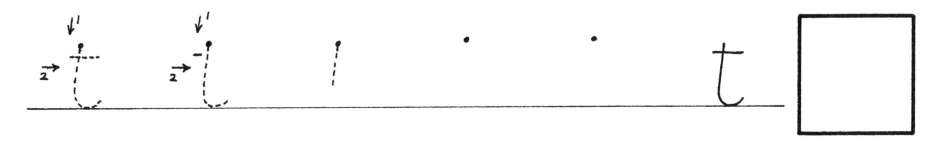

turkey

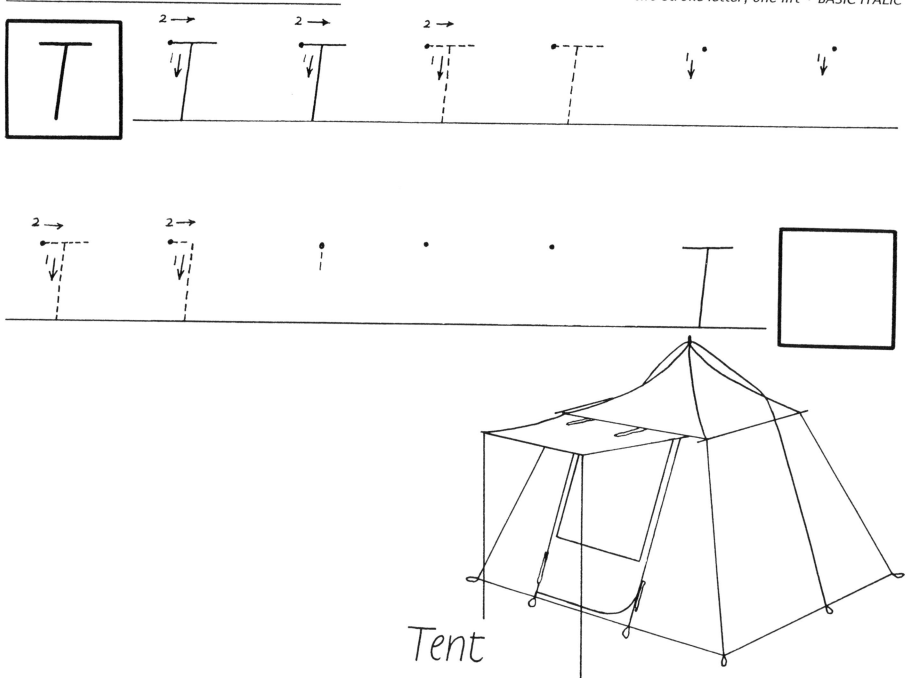

Tent

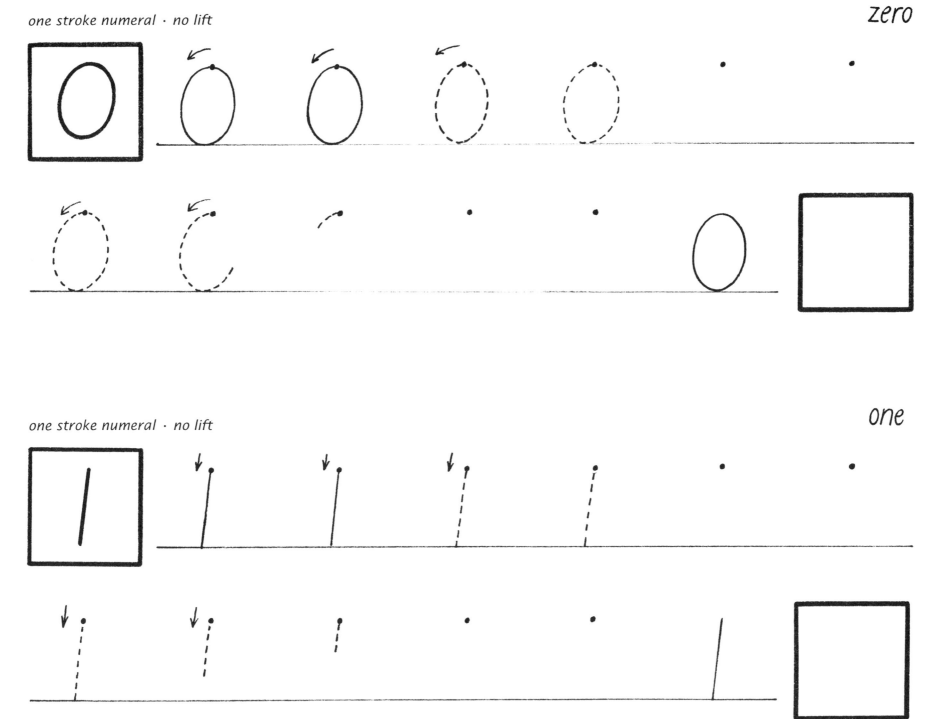

one stroke numeral · no lift **zero**

one stroke numeral · no lift **one**

© *Getty/Dubay 1994*

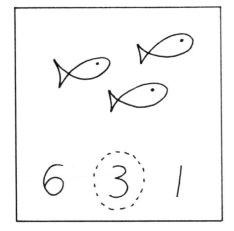

6 3 1

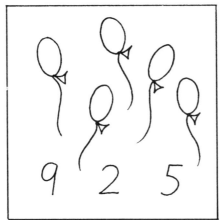

9 2 5

7 0 4

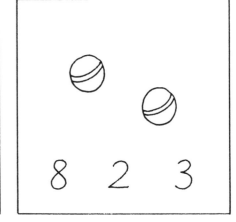

8 2 3

3 4 2

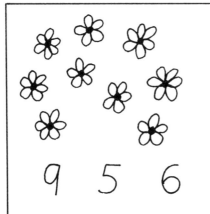

9 5 6

7 1 6

2 8 6

*Ask the student to circle the numeral
that stands for the number of objects in the box.*

one stroke numeral · no lift

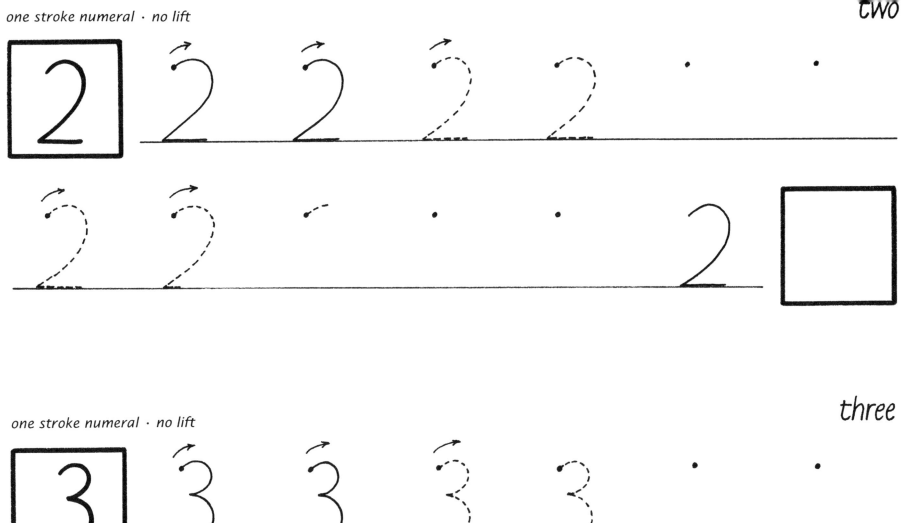

one stroke numeral · no lift

eight

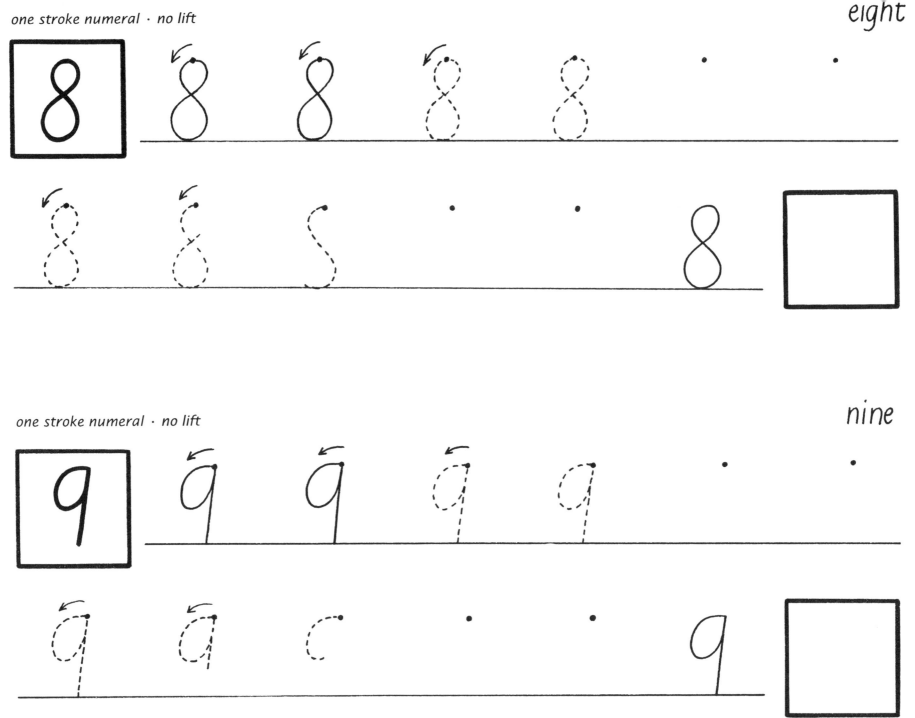

one stroke numeral · no lift

nine

31

two stroke numeral · one lift

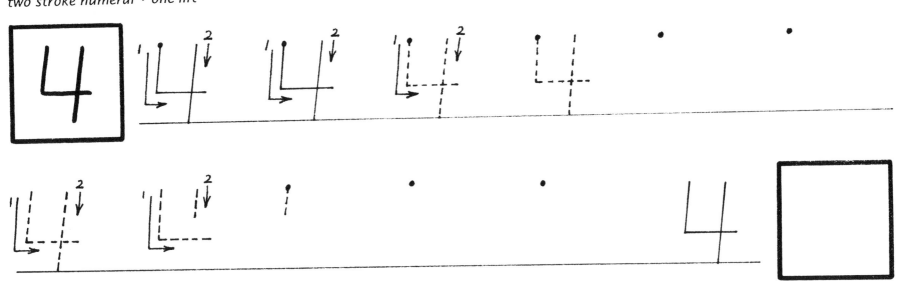

two stroke numeral · one lift

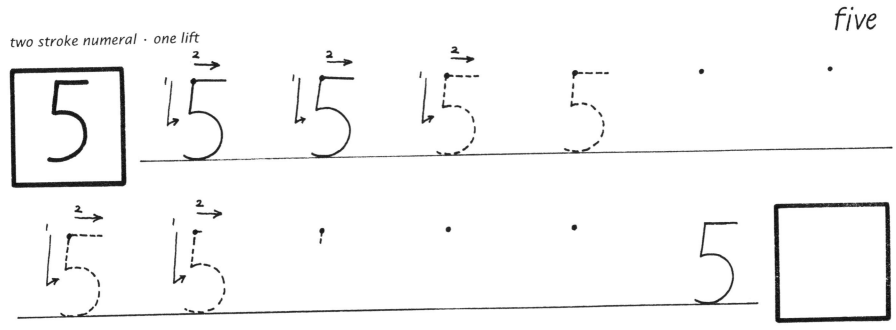

one stroke numeral · no lift

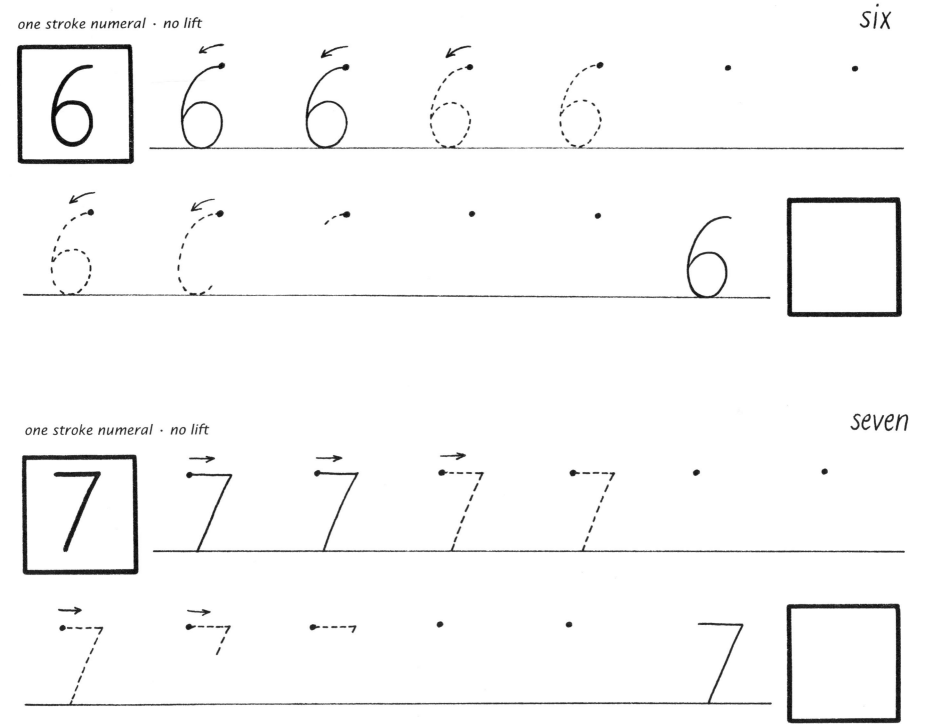

one stroke numeral · no lift